To: Avery

Attributes of a Princess

a friend of mine! ☺

by <u>Renae Frey</u> & Estelle BigEagle

May you always know
how very special you are!
from the ♡,

Uncle Steve & Aunt Vickie

This book is dedicated to my precious
granddaughter, Princess Little Bit. You have brought
more joy to my life than I could ever imagine.
-Renae Frey

This book is dedicated to my beautiful granddaughter,
Princess Sweet Pea, who brings joy to everyone whose
life she touches, and all the other princesses in my life,
both past and present, who bless my life with richness.
-Estelle BigEagle

A is for Attentive.

Alert, considerate, courteous, focused, intentional, polite, thoughtful.

It is always important to be attentive
to other's needs.

Princess Little Bit is attentive and looks for
someone that may be sad or hurt.

B is for Brave.

Bold, courageous, daring, fearless, gallant, heroic, valiant.

A princess is brave and stands up for others and for ideas that she believes in.

Princess Sweet Pea is courageous, even if others are not being kind. She helped return her friend's ball when it was taken away.

C is for Complimentary.

Acclamation, admiration, approving, commendable, praises others.

Princesses always speak highly of others.

Princess Little Bit finds the good things to say about people. She recognizes her friend's talent and compliments her.

D is for Determined.

Firm, intentional, resolute, resolved, sure.

A Princess is determined to do her very best at whatever she does.

Princess Sweet Pea pratices running everyday before the race, so that she can run as fast as she can on race day.

E is for Enthusiastic.

Avid, eager, excited, keen, ready, willing, passionate.

A princess is enthusiastic and excited.

Princess Little Bit enthusiastically cheers for her friend.

F is for Faithful.

True to one's word, steadfast, loyal, reliable, trusted.

A princess is faithful in all that she does.

Princess Sweet Pea is there when her friend is in need.

G is for Grateful.

Thankful, appreciative, glad, pleased.

A princess is always grateful for what she has.

Princess Little Bit is thankful for every gift
and kindness, and remembers to
write thank you notes.

H is for Helpful.

Useful, beneficial, valuable, practical.

Princesses are helpful and kind to others.

Princess Sweet Pea loves helping her friends
in any way that she can.

I is for Ingenious.

Clever, brilliant, imaginative, inventive, original, creative.

A princess loves to come up with ingenious and creative ideas.

Princess Little Bit dreams about what she can make next.

J is for Jovial.

Jolly, cheerful, merry, good-humored, joyful, blissful, gleeful.

Princesses should be jovial and cheerful at all times.

Princess Sweet Pea is joyful even when she might not feel like it.

K is for Kind.

Generous, considerate, gracious, sympathetic, gentle, thoughtful.

A princess is kind, gentle, helpful and nice.

Princess Little Bit loves being kind to others
and helps them when they get hurt.

L is for Loyal.

Faithful, devoted, dependable, dedicated, steadfast, trustworthy.

Princesses are faithful and dependable, when they say that they will do something, they do it.

Princess Sweet Pea helps her neighbor carry in her groceries.

M is for Moral.

Right, just, ethical, honest, good, decent, upright, virtuous.

A princess never keeps something
that isn't hers.

Princess Little Bit returns things
to their rightful owner.

N is for Neat.

Clean, orderly, organized, tidy, well kept.

A princess keeps her bedroom neat and tidy
and helps around the house.

Princess Sweet Pea works hard to keep her
bedroom clean.

O is for Obedient.

Dutiful, compliant, loyal, yielding, well-behaved, peaceful, disciplined.

A princess always minds her parents and teachers.

Princess Little Bit is obedient and listens when her parents ask her to help clear the table after tea.

P is for Polite.

Courteous, gracious, respectful, well-mannered, tactful, refined.

A princess shows good manners, says "please" and "thank you", takes turns and is careful not to hurt someone else's feelings.

Princess Sweet Pea uses great table manners.

Q is for Quality.

Value, merit, worth, caliber, excellence.

A princess always does her very best.

Princess Little Bit studies hard so that she gets good grades at school.

R is for Reliable.

Trustworthy, dependable, faithful, loyal, steadfast.

A princess is reliable, when she says that she will help, she will.

Princess Sweet Pea loves helping her neighbor plant flowers.

S is for Sociable.

Friendly, amiable, congenial, cordial, gregarious.

A princess makes others feel welcome.

Princess Little Bit loves to make others feel special and invites them to dress up parties.

T is for Trustworthy.

Reliable, dependable, honest, honorable, truthful.

A princess is always honest and can always be trusted.

Princess Sweet Pea does not say mean or hurtful things and is never rude.

U is for Understanding.

Sympathetic, compassionate, kind, sensitive, forgiving.

A princess is considerate of other people's feelings.

Princess Little Bit listens and is understanding when her friend has a tough day.

V is for Virtuous.

Good, decent, moral, honest, has integrity.

Princesses always tell the truth and accept responsibility for her actions.

Princess Sweet Pea is honest and tells the truth when her mom asks her if she broke the vase.

W is for Wise.

Sensible, smart, shrewd, rational, intelligent, bright, knowledgeable.

A princess is a wise judge of character.

Princess Little Bit is careful to choose friends
that are kind and gentle.

X is for eXtraordinary.

Remarkable, exceptional, outstanding, amazing, special.

A princess is extraordinary at making others feel special.

Princess Sweet Pea always serves her friends first.

Y is for Yielding.

Flexible, compliant, accepting, accommodating.

A princess values other's opinions.

Princess Little Bit lets her friends decide
what game to play.

Zz is for Zealous.

Enthusiastic, diligent, driven, devoted, earnest, perseverance.

A princess gets her work done with great zeal.

Princess Sweet Pea works hard in her garden,
even when the work is difficult.

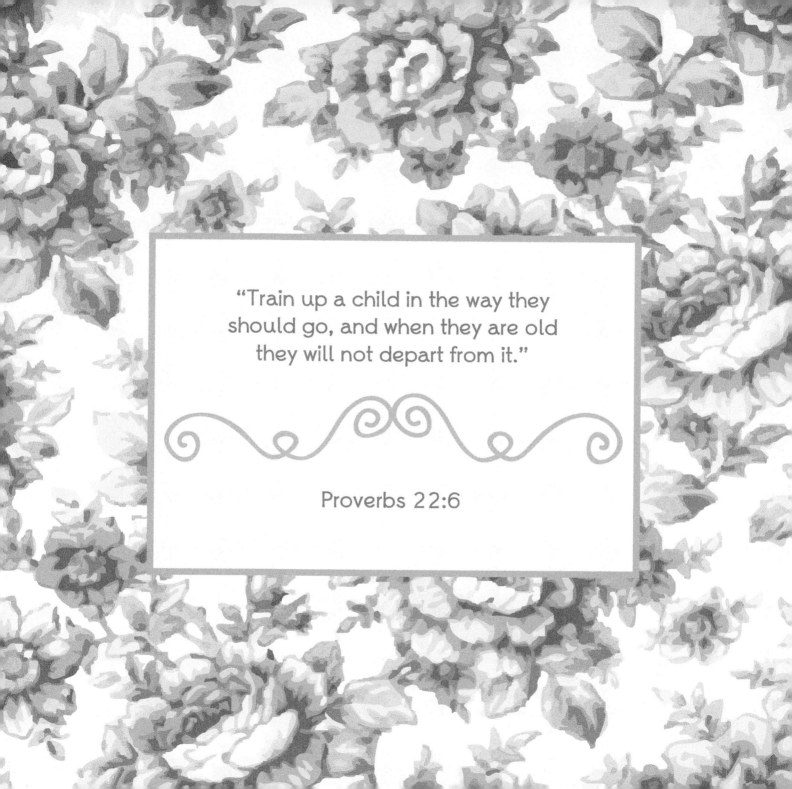

"Train up a child in the way they should go, and when they are old they will not depart from it."

Proverbs 22:6